SUNDAY EXPRESS & DAILY EXPRESS
CARTOONS

Twenty-eighth Series

A DAILY EXPRESS PUBLICATION

50p

INTRODUCTION

by

MIKE

YARWOOD

When you have finally thumbed through this Giles
cartoon book I suggest you put it away for
a few weeks and then go through it again,
I did and I found myself laughing at
the same cartoons a second time. I even
noticed things I hadn't spotted before.

Giles has not only got a wonderful sense
of humour he is also a fine artist. His
cartoons are not scribbled they are carefully
constructed. With most cartoonists you get a
single laugh out of a cartoon, with Giles you
can get as many as a dozen.

It is nice to be able to laugh at life and
Giles is one of those unique humourists
who can make us do just that. Long may
he continue to do so.

Mike Yarwood...

"I must remember to have a word with my chauvinist pig about his latest choice in caddies."

Sunday Express, September 23rd, 1973

"Right ho, chaps—the Royal Romance is officially denied. You will now cut cards for the privilege of ordering a whip-round for the wedding present."

Daily Express, September 25th, 1973

"Is that the plumber? I think my Grandma has sprung a leak in her Think Tank."

Daily Express, September 27th, 1973

"Yes, Madam, I am checking to see if the place is bugged— I mean electronically, of course."

Daily Express, October 2nd, 1973

"Did I hear correctly, son? You think Mr. Healey is right and can you borrow my car to go to Blackpool?"

Daily Express, October 4th, 1973

"Very well, Prime Minister—we'll see you round here about four p.m. then we'll all be able to explain your Phase 3 to you."

Sunday Express, October 7th, 1973

"We all know what sort of day THIS is going to be—food subsidies turned down and farm workers' wages turned up."

Daily Express, October 9th, 1973

"Why isn't George fighting at the Front? George, why aren't you fighting at the Front?"

Daily Express, October 11th, 1973

"Come, Agnes, petrol rationing is not as imminent as all that."

Sunday Express, October 14th, 1973

"The advantage, of course, of buying two or three models is that you will get two or three petrol rations."

Daily Express, October 17th, 1973

"Listen most carefully O my beauties, O stars of the East, tho' Allah blesseth our Russian ally, anyone found concealing a single copy of Karl Marx will most surely be for the chop."

Daily Express, October 18th, 1973

"Never mind the potted plants—where's me telegram from the Queen?"

Sunday Express, October 21st, 1973

"Music hath charms, Charlie boy."

Daily Express, October 23rd, 1973

"Mr. Root! Miss Powell! It's not as cold as all that!"

Daily Express, October 25th, 1973

"Our nuclear alert sure put the clock back in this neck of the woods."

Sunday Express, October 28th, 1973

"The age old custom of flogging Army equipment is one thing, the disposal of the Queen's coach horses to would-be petrol economists is another."

Daily Express, October 30th, 1973

"A man called and sold Vera a lorry load of radiators cheap as he says there is going to be a shortage."

Daily Express, November 1st, 1973

"O.K. fellas, I have apprehended the missing sparklers."

Sunday Express, November 4th, 1973

"Your mother will have to do Manchester and back in better time than that—we've got Tuesday's papers before yesterday's."

Daily Express, November 6th, 1973

"Poor Mama couldn't have taken it worse if the Bolsheviks had taken over Buckingham Palace."

Daily Express, November 8th, 1973

"I trust the ingredients of our bangers and beans have been mixed with the same loving care as HRH's cake."

Sunday Express, November 11th, 1973

"If his mother-in-law ain't sitting howling why's mine?"

Daily Express, November 13th, 1973

"Now if you'll all come to my office we'll have a game spotting the day-off-for-colds, day-off-for-backaches, etc., among yesterday's wedding crowds."

Daily Express, November 15th, 1973

"They're selling them off at the Playboy Club."

Sunday Express, November 18th, 1973

"I'm not hoarding, it's empty, but I like to give the Gestapo next door something to report."

Daily Express, November 20th, 1973

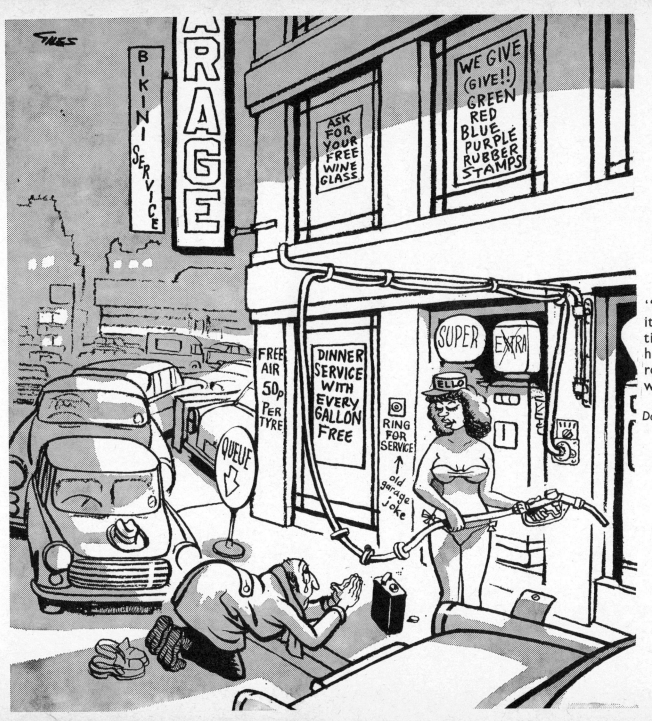

"What would you like with it, luv? Stamps, wineglasses, tiger tails, or one on the hooter if you come grovelling round here once more this week."

Daily Express, November 22nd, 1973

"As the Good Book tells us '. . . he heapeth up riches, and knoweth not who shall gather them'."

Sunday Express, November 25th, 1973

"If she's given you petrol coupons by mistake, there's probably some poor Jag owner whooping it up on your old age pension bonus. Heh! Heh! Heh!"

Daily Express, November 29th, 1973

"Well, there's one place where I bet they're not short of fuel."

"Left foot, then your right foot, there's a good boy! Beastly Arabs, making our poor Algy walk to school."

Daily Express, December 4th, 1973

"Mummy—want to know one reason why Dad's car has been doing more miles to the gallon than yours?"

Daily Express, December 6th, 1973

"I'd believe the theory that once you've ridden a bike you can always ride a bike if everybody wouldn't keep saying 'Cheerio'."

Sunday Express, December 9th, 1973

"Isn't it wonderful, Mum—Mark's tummy's better and the Burtons are together again."

Daily Express, December 11th, 1973

"RIGHT! Which of you comedians said one way to warm up a draughty cabin is to set light to the driver?"

Daily Express, December 13th, 1973

"If we told the cops how long Grandma's been reading in there with a light on, she'd be good for three months in Holloway."

Sunday Express, December 16th, 1973

"Bed at 10.30 don't suit him nor me neither—made me get up and go for a bike ride at 5 a.m."

Daily Express, December 18th, 1973

HEATING
RESTRICTIONS

MAXIMUM OFFICE
TEMPERATURE

63°F
(17·25°C)

PENALTIES

"Methinks the Chairman'
Fahrenheit reading is we
above the permitte
allocation."

Daily Express, December 20th, 197

"You lot aren't here to bring me comfort and joy—you're here to save your blooming light and heating at home."

Sunday Express, December 23rd, 1973

Olly O!!

all creatures great and small.

mr giles's Christmas aunts arriving

When they asked Mr. Giles how he was going to spend Christmas, he said: "No comment." So as I expect this one will be exactly the same as all his other 100-odd Christmases here is this Christmas forecast. First thing he does is to round up all his aunts nephews and neices and their aunts nephews and nieces etc. And bring them all to the house in one go in a cattle float. Coming from a jockey family they're not very high. And all walk under the table without bending down and put their hats on a chair.

head aunt

They're the same little black hats and coats they had when Mr. Giles was four.

And I once got a thick Christmas ear for saying they look like a flock of little rooks (not the Jean version). They have a very happy festive season sitting round the fire humming of wintergreen ointment and embrocation. And chatting ailments.

Ollyfied mr giles ↑ my joke!

Daily Express, December 24th, 1973

And making whispers about Mr. Giles' habits which you can hear half a mile away. His head aunt keeps looking in his direction shaking her head and saying: "Pity." Mr. Giles is never very happy the rest of the year, but Christmas time he's 10 times worse.

merry mr giles waiting to greet merry jean rook →

His Head Aunt says the only way he and his mates could make Christmas different to the rest of the year would be for them to go on the wagon.

He got very jumpy when the paper told him his old mate Jean-Ground-Glass-and-Acid was coming down to write a piece about him and Christmas. He worked out a rota for us all to go out and buy every edition it was in throughout the land. But I think Jean Rook is very nice and wouldn't half have given him a dusting. Ah, well, it only comes once a year —and I expect the New Year will be worse. Merry Easter.

P.S. Vera's got her Christmas cold which usually lasts till next Christmas.

Noel.

yours truly, giles junor

Daily Express, December 24th, 1973

"What do you mean—they say they needn't go back till next Wednesday?"

Daily Express, December 27th, 1973

"That wasn't a nice thing to say about Mrs. Turner's new baby—Some Mothers Do 'ave 'em."

Sunday Express, December 30th, 1973

"The lady wishes to know if they've taxed wind yet. Have they taxed wind yet, Harry?"

Daily Express, January 3rd, 1974

"Do you think it would infringe the principles of his three-day week if he joined our seven-day week and let down a few balloons?"

Sunday Express, January 6th, 1974

"Well, that's all right, lads. 11.0 Matins; early lunch; kick-off 3.0;
back here by 5.30; wash and brush up and a cup of tea; Evensong 6.30."

Daily Express, January 8th, 1974

"You can come out now—it was only Bertie bursting a paper bag."

Daily Express, January 10th, 1974

"They wouldn't be singing their little heads off if they could read."

Sunday Express, January 13th, 1974

"Goodness, no trains? Whatever's been going on during my Christmas recess?"

Daily Express, January 15th, 1974

"O.K. Grandma, I've found the little top ones you dropped—Butch has got 'em in his basket."

Daily Express, January 17th, 1974

"Bloody fine match this is going to be—rationed to one toilet roll each."

Sunday Express, January 20th, 1974

"You're good boys to think of paper saving, but I don't think daddy will like you cutting up his paper before he's read it."

Daily Express, January 22nd, 1974

"That's Grandma's fuel saving for the day—good night party political broadcast."

Daily Express, January 24th, 1974

"I *know* you only came to New Zealand as a hundred metre sprinter, lad . . ."

Sunday Express, January 27th, 1974

"Not in my house you don't!"

Daily Express, January 29th, 1974

"Do I detect a less fervent support of the train drivers' cause now that he can't get to his team's away match because of no trains on Sunday?"

Sunday Express, February 3rd, 1974

"Dad! Isn't it smashing—
we've got two feet of snow."

Daily Express, February 7th, 1974

"You are entitled to your own political beliefs regardless of race, religion or colour, but you will kindly refrain from calling the rest of us 'Brothers'."

Sunday Express, February 10th, 1974

"Careful with this one—he had Jeremy Thorpe yesterday."

Daily Express, February 12th, 1974

"Right! Which one's the cupid?"

Daily Express, February 14th, 1974

" 'He is charming, law-abiding, persuasive, a man of great judgment and integrity, trustworthy, and beyond corruption'. So we vote for his opponent."

Sunday Express, February 17th, 1974

"As a matter of fact, Madam, I'm not one of your plaguey party canvassers—I'm from the Pools to tell you you've come up with a First Dividend win."

Daily Express, February 19th, 1974

"In our business, nurse, all men are equal. Now give Mr. Kinley his bottle even if his politics are a slightly different shade from yours."

Daily Express, February 21st, 1974

"That's one large Martini down the drain—she said 'Thanks comrade'."

Sunday Express, February 24th, 1974

"Everyone else in the road have had their polling cards, Butch. I repeat—everyone else in the road have had their polling cards, Butch . . ."

Daily Express, February 26th, 1974

"You've had my vote with your fuel saving, back-to-the-wall campaign, I like me trips to the Polls by Rolls."

Daily Express, February 28th, 1974

"It's Charlie—when the hell are we going to bring him ashore to have his vote."

Sunday Express, March 3rd, 1974

"If they're going to have another election they're not coming round the second time kissing and patting us on our heads."

Daily Express, March 5th, 1974

"I am not concerned with what is currently popular in the United States, I give everybody three minutes to streak-on cassocks and surplices starting from NOW."

Sunday Express, March 10th, 1974

"First M.P. over that step in his birthday suit—POW!!"

Daily Express, March 12th, 1974

"Come off it, Harry. Bringing back hanging as a deterrent to Streaking is a bit thick."

Daily Express, March 14th, 1974

"Honestly Ref, I only meant to belt him one—I didn't mean to exorcise him."

"Awake, beloved, control your feverish impatience to learn the result of last night's voting in the House."

Daily Express, March 19th, 1974

"As a matter of fact I do not think this compensates for missing the opening of the Flat."

Daily Express, March 21st, 1974

"I tell you every year it's a waste of money buying your Mother flowers for Mother's Day."

Sunday Express, March 24th, 1974

"Grandma will be letting off howls of anguish if Mr. Healey finds out she's got a Haig bottle full of sixpences under her bed."

Daily Express, March 26th, 1974

"And don't you keep a-looking at me, yer varmint."

Daily Express, March 28th, 1974

"When m'Lord has been using public transport a little longer he'll notice we don't take cheques or I.O.U.s."

Sunday Express, March 31st, 1974

"Everybody out, Sir, this is as far as we go at 55p a gallon."

Daily Express, April 2nd, 1974

"Mummy says if a fifth of a mile, 13 storeys high boat, weighing 60,000 tons, can get stuck at sea, we've had her for crew this year."

Daily Express, April 4th, 1974

"I think Father likes your new boyfriend, he's letting him help with some land reclamation."

Sunday Express, April 7th, 1974

"Never mind Enoch Powell's baloney about doctors being nurses' perks—where's me dinner?"

Daily Express, April 11th, 1974

"As a matter of fact I did read that a doctors' journal said that swearing is good for you—but not that good."

Sunday Express, April 14th, 1974

"Our office cleansing operator wants to know if it's all right to bring her children with her until the holidays are over."

Daily Express, April 16th, 1974

"Now you and me are going to have a little chat about the facts of life. Lesson One: We're all going to stop calling me 'Duckie'."

Daily Express, April 18th, 1974

"Nurse Rigg here will patch you up, she's very good with football riff-raff. Her team lost yesterday, by the way."

Sunday Express, April 21st, 1974

"Listen, mate, a whack from my missus is one thing—but one from yours is another."

Daily Express, April 25th, 1974

"Militant wives are bad enough during the week."

Sunday Express, April 28th, 1974

"Lady, you don't happen to have one about horses being unfair to riders?"

Daily Express, April 30th, 1974

"Buying my secretary chocolates every day may well be considered as a bribe in high places."

Daily Express, May 2nd, 1974

"The Cup Final and Newmarket falling on the same day as our jumble sale was adversary enough, without a certain member of our congregation passing off forged raffle tickets."

Sunday Express, May 5th, 1974

"You've made your blooming minds up too soon! He's not going back till he's finished his ironing."

Daily Express, May 9th, 1974

"He says if an anonymous benefactor comes to the rescue of our wage claims it won't be him."

Daily Express, May 10th, 1974

"As we haven't had beef for so long I thought I'd be rash and treat ourselves to a piece of sirloin."

Sunday Express, May 12th, 1974

"Putting children up for adoption on TV has started something."

Daily Express, May 14th, 1974

"A funny thing happened to old Charlie while you were on strike, nurse."

Daily Express, May 16th, 1974

"Which is the one you say is a grossly overpaid old crow?"

Sunday Express, May 19th, 1974

"Father, we know the students got their rise and you're hard up, but we simply do not want to buy a pig."

Daily Express, May 21st, 1974

"Besides the normal opportunities for fame and fortune, like bank and train robberies, there are now lucrative careers like kidnapping royalty, becoming a national hero peddling dope in Turkey . . ."

Daily Express, May 23rd, 1974

"I hope you'll keep an eye on them, it's the first time they've been to sea."

Sunday Express, May 26th, 1974

"I brought my smile to work and all I got was: 'What the hell are you grinning at?'"

Daily Express, May 30th, 1974

"Did you or did you not inform the patient that if you had one squeak out of him you'd match his other eye up?"

Daily Express, June 1st, 1974

"It's very nice of you to agree with Her Majesty's tribute to our being overworked, undervalued, never overpaid—but I'm still going to book you."

Sunday Express, June 2nd, 1974

"You two, don't forget the order of the day—peaceful co-habitation and none of the old Kung Fu."

Daily Express, June 4th, 1974

"A French horse favourite for the Derby hasn't improved his love for the Common Market. Especially as he backed it to win."

Daily Express, June 6th, 1974

"Pvt. 909587213A won't be joining us this morning, Sarge. He's on hunger strike so he can be sent home."

Sunday Express, June 9th, 1974

"I may be a chauvinist pig in your eyes, Miss Tamworth, but I prefer not to have my elevenses in a trough."

Daily Express, June 11th, 1974

"Just one thing, fellas—you were supposed to dig this hole two hundred yards down the road."

Daily Express, June 13th, 1974

"Here comes a male chauvinist pig if ever I saw one."

Daily Express, June 15th, 1974

"Wake up, dear, 'tis Father's Day. Joint presentation—one jar of tadpoles."

"You say 'Your Majesty' if you bump into the Queen. Not to Jean Rook."

Daily Express, June 18th, 1974

Battle Royal Ascot. Football techniques come to the sport of kings.

Daily Express, June 20th, 1974

"Looks like your kids read that thing this week which said children should be allowed to take up drinking at home."

Daily Express, June 22nd, 1974

"Dashed good piece of luck, Harry, your second gardener being in hospital same time as you."

Sunday Express, June 23rd, 1974

"Dad, why do we have to have 'Scotland the Brave' all through breakfast just because Grandma's got a wee sister in Aberdeen?"

Daily Express, June 25th, 1974

"We've been here hours. I hope those Security Officers who took all our luggage for a check WERE Security Officers."

Daily Express, June 27th, 1974

"The car's right outside, dear. Drove straight into London Airport without being checked by one of 'em!"

Daily Express, June 29th, 1974

"Oh dear, Daddy isn't going to like this. Our new union member is wearing a cap."

Sunday Express, June 30th, 1974

"And if you accept any invitations to see their bloody holiday war films you're on your own!"

Daily Express, July 25th, 1974

"Awake, luv? The consultant said he'll be back to stitch you up in about a fortnight."

Daily Express, July 6th, 1974

"You know how it is—'If Rosewall can reach the finals at Wimbledon at his age . . .'"

here we go again!

ha ha ... grr

Read all about the laughter makers in the effer~~vescent~~ Daily Express ho ho ho.

Well i can give you some first hand information as to what makes one 'Laughter Maker' laugh. Nothing much. (1st hand 2nd hand) One thing that i refer to mr giles the cartoonist (see this paper sometimes) doesn't make him very happy is whatever time he goes to bed he has to get up very early in the morning and read all the newspapers all the morning to get an idea for the next morning's express. although we are all interned in one end of the house and he's right up the other end we can still hear him grumbling away about everything and the world in general. And it's not a very good thing to for us to get caught laughing either. the other morning little old punchinello giles was crawling down to get the papers in his happy morning mood and unfortunatly mr butch our airdale had left one of his little t bones at the bottom of the stairs which became wedged between mr g's big toe and the next one. he carried on into the kitchen which has a stone farmhouse floor and was looking around to see where the little tapping noise was coming from at such a early hour. i thought that was very funny but not for long.

Daily Express, July 9th, 1974

a lot of things don't make him laugh, like the milkman wissling "you are my sunshine", little bits of carbide in his tea, everybody, anybody who says good morning when it aint, or asks him how he is when he maintains they don't really care how he is and that it's none of there bluw business anyway. **We** are all very quiet breakfast time and all you can hear is **grandma's** tummy rumbling and an occassional funny noise from **butch.** once we heard a little "glonk" from **aunty** Vera taking one of her pills but only once as mr laughing-gas-giles makes her take them after he has gone to work now. **which is another thing he don't like. he thinks** his cartoons are very funny while he's doing them but blows his top when he sees them in the paper next morning and doesn't think they're funny at all and nor do **i.** **ah well,** i could fill the rest of the paper with **REAL** stories behind the scenes with minnihaha-**giles** but for safety's sake **i** wont.

yours truly,
watch out for your Express Smiles
every day   ho ho ho again,

giles junor.

P.S. they tell me he thinks everythings funny when he's in his pub.

rumble rumble

Daily Express, July 9th, 1974

"Caviar, peacock in aspic, chips, beans and char twice, luv."

Daily Express, July 11th, 1974

"Here we are, pundits, opportunity knocks. 'Liverpool and Leeds want the best manager money can buy to follow two of the most successful men in the history of the game'."

Sunday Express, July 14th, 1974

"Same with mine—'Your boy swallowing a new $\frac{1}{2}$p. does not constitute an emergency.'"

Daily Express, July 16th, 1974